2002
QUESTIONS
AND ANSWERS
FOR
LOVERS

Other titles by
Cyndi Haynes and Dale Edwards

2002 Romantic Ideas

2002 Things to Do on a Date

2002 Ways to Find, Attract, and Keep a Mate

2000 Ways to Say "I Love You"

2002
QUESTIONS
AND ANSWERS
FOR
LOVERS

Fun, Romantic & Revealing

Cyndi Haynes & Dale Edwards

Adams Media Corporation
Holbrook, Massachusetts

Published by
Adams Media Corporation
260 Center Street, Holbrook, MA 02343

ISBN: 1-58062-225-9

Printed in Canada.

J I H G F E D C B

Library of Congress Cataloging-in-Publication Data
Haynes, Cyndi.
2002 questions & answers for lovers /
Cyndi Haynes & Dale Edwards.
p.   cm.
ISBN 1-58062-225-9
1. Mate selection—Miscellanea. 2. Dating (Social customs)—Miscellanea. 3. Single people—Miscellanea. 4. Man-woman relationships—Miscellanea. I. Title: 2002 questions and answers for lovers. II. Edwards, Dale. III. Title.
HQ801.H3722000
646.7'7—dc21
99-046339

This book is available at quantity discounts for bulk purchases. For information, call 1-800-872-5627.

Visit our home page at http://www.adamsmedia.com

Dedicated to Andrew,
who never ceases to amaze us with his love.
Our world is infinitely better because you are in it.
Thank you!

ACKNOWLEDGMENTS

After almost eight years of marriage and lots of books, there are many wonderful people to thank for their help along the way. We know that any successful undertaking requires the support and guidance of others, so we want to take this opportunity to thank a few of our biggest supporters.

First, Bob Adams for always believing in our books. You and all of the terrific people at Adams Media Corporation continue to be a major blessing to us. We are so glad to be among your authors.

Edward Walters, Editor in Chief, your suggestions and help have always made our manuscripts much better and your kindness along the way has not gone unnoticed.

Will McNeill, your editing is meticulous and you are always glad to answer our questions. Every author should be so lucky.

Wayne Jackson, Director of Marketing, you do a fabulous job and we appreciate your hard work more than we can say.

Marme, Annie, and Charlie, for always being there. We love you with all of our hearts. Our time together is pure bliss.

Fritzie, we love you so very much! You are a dear lady and your support has always meant the world to us.

Finally, for Wally, who in his plow horse manner always manages to be the support and earthly rock that we need. We wouldn't trade you for the world! You are indeed our soul mate!

Dear Fellow Romantic,

Each year thousands upon thousands of couples walk down the aisle with the hope of a life of happily ever after together.

One of the biggest mistakes couples make is getting caught up in the grand emotion of romance and planning a beautiful wedding instead of spending adequate time finding out if they are, in fact, compatible. You need to use your common sense as well as your emotions when choosing a life partner!

This book contains two kinds of questions. The first set of questions has multiple answers—to encourage you to think about every area of your life, including your dreams and goals. The second set of questions is open ended—to encourage you to ponder your responses.

Some of these questions may not be easy for you to answer. Take your time when answering and be honest with yourself. The questions were written to help the two of you unearth your individual preferences, habits, goals, dreams, and deepest desires.

The best way to use this book is to read it through on your own and truthfully answer all of the questions. Next, give it to your significant other and ask him to do the same. Finally, go through the book together with open hearts and open eyes.

Keep in mind, being compatible doesn't mean that you are carbon copies of each other. It just means that the two of you can live in harmony together despite your differences.

We wrote our first book, *2002 Things to Do on a Date,* when we were dating and we have learned a great deal about relationships since then. We know that it takes love, hard work, and a strong commitment to make a great marriage. However, all of the work is worth it when you know in your heart that you are indeed married to your soul mate. Finding the right person and being with the right person is definitely worth the work and the wait.

Happy relationships!

The course of true love never did run smooth.

—SHAKESPEARE

FOR YOUR INFORMATION:

My ideal mate would:
- ○ Make me a huge priority in his/her life
- ○ Have a full life without me and wouldn't place demands on my time
- ○ Think of me as a best friend
- ○ Think of us as being two peas in a pod
- ○ Put my interests before his/her own

My longest relationship, before my current one, lasted:
- ○ Less than a month
- ○ Six months to a year
- ○ A year or two
- ○ I have never had a long-term relationship

When a match has equal partners, then I fear not.

—AESCHYLUS

I think that the most important traits in a mate are:
- ○ Faithfulness
- ○ Good looks
- ○ High morals
- ○ Sense of humor
- ○ Honesty
- ○ Sex appeal
- ○ Romantic nature
- ○ Adventurous spirit

The most important part of a relationship for me, is:
- O Companionship
- O Sex
- O Love
- O Romance
- O Passion
- O Being a part of a couple
- O Becoming parents together
- O Being accepted into society as an adult

There is entirely too much worrying about unhappy marriages. All marriages are happy. It's only the living together afterward that causes the trouble.

—LOUISVILLE COURIER-JOURNAL

I want a significant other who is my:
- O Lover
- O Best friend
- O Confidant
- O Mentor

My philosophy about relationships can best be summed up by:
- O Love makes the world go round
- O Love hurts
- O Love is the icing on the cake of life
- O Love stinks
- O Love is something that happens only to others

> *He who marries might be sorry.*
> *He who does not will be sorry.*
>
> —*CZECHOSLOVAKIAN PROVERB*

When it comes to the battle of the sexes, I believe:
- O It is a man's world
- O There isn't a battle going on, as we are all the same on the inside
- O Women won the war years ago
- O I like to make up after each battle with the enemy

When it comes to romance, my favorite things are:

O Candles	O Champagne
O Soft music	O Lingerie
O Chocolate	O Poetry
O Love letters	O Romantic getaways
O Diamonds	O Unexpected gifts
O Jewelry	O Flowers

If my significant other and I broke up, I would:
- O Start dating my ex
- O Give myself lots of time to heal my broken heart
- O Jump back into the dating scene
- O Give up on love for a very long time

The song that best describes our relationship would be a:
- O Blues number
- O Country, heartbreak ballad
- O Symphony

On a scale of one to ten, with ten being healthy and one standing for unhealthy, I would rate our relationship a:
- ○ One to three
- ○ Three to six
- ○ Six to ten
- ○ Off the charts—it is so great!

Marriage, to me, means:
- ○ Happily ever after
- ○ The end of romance
- ○ A partnership
- ○ Socially, a convenient lifestyle choice

Nobody tells you—women still do a lot more housework than men.

Commitment, to me, means:
- ○ Forever
- ○ The marriage will last as long as we are both happy in the relationship

My idea of the most romantic couple is:
- ○ Romeo and Juliet
- ○ My closest friend's romantic relationship
- ○ My mom and dad
- ○ My significant other and me

The most popular reasons that couples get married:
Love
Security
Companionship
To have children
Social pressure

The most important responsibility of being a mate is:
- ○ Providing financial support
- ○ Being a sexual partner
- ○ Being a best friend
- ○ Becoming a parent

My idea of togetherness is:
- ○ Always and forever
- ○ Never apart, except under extreme circumstances
- ○ Space in our togetherness
- ○ Two peas in a pod
- ○ Lots and lots of breathing room

Lovers never get tired of each other,
because they are always talking about themselves.
—LA ROCHEFOUCAULD

The main reason that I want to get married is:
- ○ Love
- ○ To have children
- ○ Sex
- ○ Because my friends are all married
- ○ I want to settle down
- ○ It is the grown-up thing to do

What I look for in a mate, in order of importance, is:
- ○ Looks, personality, brains
- ○ Personality, brains, looks
- ○ Brains, personality, looks

If my fiancé had a bachelor party, I would:
- ○ Think that it was great
- ○ Think that it was archaic
- ○ Resent it
- ○ Feel very left out
- ○ Feel a bit jealous

If my significant other went away for a long weekend, I would:
- ○ Thrive and enjoy being alone
- ○ Feel sad and miss her/him the entire time
- ○ Resent her/his trip without me
- ○ Show up and surprise her/him

If I see my significant other when she/he is sick, tired, or dressed sloppily, I feel:
- ○ A little bit repulsed
- ○ Turned off, but who wouldn't feel like that?
- ○ That this is great that we can be so relaxed and natural with each other
- ○ The same way as I always do—madly in love!

Working on our relationship means:
- ○ Talking more openly
- ○ Going to a therapist
- ○ Reading self-help books
- ○ Attending a couples' retreat
- ○ Signing up for a relationship seminar

I believe that a couple should be engaged for:
- ○ Three months or less
- ○ Three to six months
- ○ Six months to a year
- ○ Longer than a year

I feel that couples should date at least _____ before they become engaged.
- ○ Three years or more
- ○ Two years or more
- ○ A year or more
- ○ Six months
- ○ At least once—real love doesn't have a time line!

If you ever expect to be loved,
you must reveal who you are.

—*LEO BUSCAGLIA*

I believe that the main purpose of an engagement is to:
- ○ Plan the wedding
- ○ Iron out our differences
- ○ Make sure that we are right for one another
- ○ Get emotionally prepared for marriage
- ○ Enroll in couples' therapy
- ○ Work on setting up housekeeping
- ○ Celebrate our relationship with family and friends

My feelings about engagement rings are:
- ○ The bigger the better
- ○ Size doesn't matter—it is the thought that counts
- ○ I want it to be a family heirloom
- ○ They are silly, pretentious, and old-fashioned
- ○ It should be the nicest that one can afford as it will last a lifetime

Whoever is happy will make others happy too.

—ANNE FRANK

I believe that a couple should:
- ○ Ask their parents for permission to marry
- ○ Ask the bride's father for permission to marry
- ○ Just announce their engagement

I would want my marriage partner to:
- ○ Always wear the wedding band I gave her/him
- ○ Wear it only on special occasions
- ○ Not wear a ring if it was her/his preference

I would want our wedding rings to:
- ○ Match
- ○ Be engraved
- ○ Cost a fortune
- ○ Be made of gold
- ○ Have diamonds
- ○ Be family heirlooms
- ○ Be antiques

Weddings should cost:
- ○ Absolutely nothing—who can put a price tag on love?
- ○ Under $5,000
- ○ Under $10,000
- ○ Under $20,000
- ○ Under $50,000
- ○ Under $100,000
- ○ It doesn't matter to me

When my significant other and I plan our wedding, I want:
- ○ My parents to be included
- ○ My significant other's parents to help
- ○ To hire a wedding planner
- ○ To get my friends to help
- ○ To get my significant other's friends to help
- ○ To plan it by myself
- ○ Just the two of us to make all of the decisions

Wedding vows should be:
- ○ Traditional
- ○ Written by the couple
- ○ Tailored by the minister to fit just us
- ○ Contemporary

When I dream about our wedding day, I always imagine:
- Beautiful music
- The vows we speak
- Gorgeous flowers
- Saying "I do"
- A beautiful bridal gown
- My ex-love being filled with envy
- Our friends being so happy for us
- Family members celebrating
- A wedding reception for the society page to write about
- Handsome men in tuxes
- Feeling madly in love

When I get married, I want to get married in:
- The church where I am a member
- A famous cathedral
- The great outdoors
- The church where my parents got married
- A storybook country church
- An exotic location
- A wedding chapel
- A beautiful service at my parents' home

The most important ingredients of a wedding reception are:
- The cake
- Open bar
- Fine champagne
- Music
- Menu
- Location
- Having my family there
- Having all of my friends in attendance
- Dancing
- Gorgeous flowers and beautiful table settings

Wedding showers should:
- ○ Be for the bride only
- ○ Be an event for the couple

The theme for a wedding shower that I would like best would be:
- ○ Household gifts
- ○ Lingerie
- ○ Around-the-clock
- ○ Wine
- ○ China, crystal, or silver
- ○ Entertainment
- ○ Holiday

For a wedding present, I think my parents will give us:
- ○ Money
- ○ A gift from our bridal registry
- ○ Something fabulous, but whimsical
- ○ Something practical
- ○ Their best wishes, but no present

I want my engagement ring to be:
- ○ A diamond
- ○ My birthstone
- ○ A pearl
- ○ A plain, simple ring
- ○ I don't like engagement rings

I plan to give my significant other an engagement gift.
- ○ True
- ○ False

I plan to give my spouse a wedding gift.
- ○ True
- ○ False

When it comes to picking a best man or maid of honor, I:
- ○ Think that both partners should approve both choices
- ○ Believe that each partner should choose his/her best friend

The last wedding that I attended made me feel:
- ○ Romantic
- ○ Heartsick
- ○ Happy
- ○ Terrified
- ○ Sappy and silly

When I picture my own wedding day, I feel:
- ○ Happy and madly in love
- ○ Scared, at least a little bit
- ○ Nervous, but good
- ○ Excited

When I think in terms of a long-term relationship, I:
- ○ Get terrified
- ○ Hear wedding bells
- ○ Feel trapped
- ○ Get excited

Nobody tells you—most arguments are about power and control.

I view divorce as:
- ○ A major catastrophe
- ○ The end of a love affair
- ○ A sad fact of life in today's world
- ○ Something that will never happen to me
- ○ The destruction of a family—to be avoided at all costs

My significant other reminds me a little bit of:
- ○ My parent
- ○ My best friend
- ○ My worst enemy
- ○ My fantasy lover

When it comes to relationships, I am best described as:
- ○ Romantic
- ○ Optimistic
- ○ Realistic and practical
- ○ A loser
- ○ Giving
- ○ Idealistic

I believe that love and romance bring:
- ○ Fulfillment
- ○ Heartache and disappointment
- ○ Joy and happiness
- ○ An increase in one's self-esteem

Tip: The best way to get what you want in a relationship is to ask for it.

When I see a married couple in a restaurant and they aren't talking, I:
- ○ Feel sad—where did their romance go?
- ○ Am determined not to end up like that
- ○ Think it is great that two people can be together and not feel obligated to have to talk all of the time
- ○ Don't pay any attention to it

The first year of marriage is:
- ○ An extended honeymoon
- ○ An adjustment period
- ○ The time to gradually go from the fairy-tale courtship to the real world

My best friends think that marriage can best be summed up as:
- ○ A dream come true
- ○ What you do when you become an adult
- ○ A natural progression of a good relationship
- ○ An end to your happy, carefree days
- ○ A romance killer
- ○ An institution, and who wants to live in an institution?

My parents' marriage is:
- ○ Very happy
- ○ Romantic
- ○ Stormy
- ○ Ordinary
- ○ Dysfunctional
- ○ Over—it ended in divorce

In my parents' marriage:
- ○ My dad was always the boss

- ○ My mom was the boss
- ○ The kids were their bosses
- ○ They were equal partners

My parents handle conflict by:
- ○ Stonewalling each other
- ○ Talking things out calmly
- ○ Yelling
- ○ Sweeping the issue under the rug

I have seen my parents argue:
- ○ Several times
- ○ A bunch
- ○ Not even once

Today, the best thing about my parents' marriage is:
- ○ Their love for one another
- ○ They stayed together
- ○ Their children—especially yours truly!
- ○ The quality of life that they made together

My parents had trouble talking about:
- ○ Finances
- ○ Sex
- ○ Feelings
- ○ Child rearing
- ○ Leisure-time activities
- ○ Health problems
- ○ In-laws
- ○ Careers
- ○ Past loves

My mother has been married:
- ○ Once
- ○ More than once

○ Never—OOPS!

My dad has been married:
- ○ Once
- ○ More than once
- ○ Never—OOPS!

My parents fought mostly about:
- ○ Money
- ○ Sex
- ○ Children
- ○ Careers
- ○ Chores around the house
- ○ Leisure time
- ○ In-laws

My parents' educational background included:
- ○ Graduation from graduate school
- ○ Graduation from college
- ○ Graduation from high school
- ○ Graduation from grade school

When it comes to male/female relationships, I can best be described as:
- ○ Very old-fashioned
- ○ Contemporary
- ○ Traditional
- ○ Unusual—I have a unique perspective
- ○ Free spirited

When it comes to broken hearts, I:
- ○ Have had my fair share
- ○ Have broken a few in my time
- ○ Have never had a broken heart
- ○ Have a heart of stone

*Only independent people can choose
to remain in a relationship.
The most mature level of love exists
only in the face of free choice.*

—*AARON STONE*

Intimacy is best described as:
- O   Sex
- O   Sharing feelings and ideas
- O   Snuggling and not having to talk
- O   The mushy stuff in romance novels

My priorities are:
- O   Spiritual growth
- O   Career
- O   My love life
- O   Children
- O   Parents
- O   Friends
- O   Pets
- O   Social life
- O   Financial success

I believe that problems in a romantic relationship are:
- O   Private—just between the couple
- O   To be discussed with close friends
- O   To be discussed only with family members
- O   Public domain

*Nobody tells you—both partners bring to the
relationship preconceived
ideas about how the relationship should be.*

If my partner had an affair, I would:
- ○ End the relationship
- ○ Forgive and forget
- ○ Go into a major depression
- ○ Get into couples' therapy
- ○ Set up an appointment with my attorney the next minute
- ○ Seek revenge

When it comes to romantic relationships, I believe that they are:
- ○ A fifty/fifty proposition
- ○ A one hundred percent effort on the part of each partner
- ○ Usually based on one partner being a giver and the other being a taker
- ○ Complicated as sometimes one person gives, and at other times the other partner does the giving. In the end it all balances out!

The animal that best describes my significant other is a:
- ○ Bear—grumpy and growly
- ○ Puppy—cute and cuddly
- ○ Cat—aloof and self-centered

- ○ Monkey—fun and zany
- ○ Bird—free and easy

If my significant other was part of the cast of characters in a murder mystery, he/she would be perfectly typecast as:
- ○ The hero/heroine
- ○ The smart detective
- ○ The victim—everyone wants to get rid of him/her
- ○ An eccentric bit player
- ○ A nice person who just happens to find the body
- ○ The murderer—OOPS!

If my significant other was part of the cast of characters in a romance novel, the novel would be set:
- ○ In a foreign land
- ○ In the past
- ○ In a gothic setting
- ○ In the present—he/she can be romantic anytime!

My mother thinks my significant other is:
- ○ Wonderful
- ○ Taking advantage of me
- ○ In need of a big dose of maturity
- ○ Needing to settle down before we get married
- ○ Not treating me very well

I believe that all great relationships:
- ○ Require hard work and commitment
- ○ Just naturally happen if you are in love
- ○ Are based solely on chemistry
- ○ Are made in Heaven
- ○ Only happen in fairy tales
- ○ Are rarer than a perfect diamond

I secretly want my mate to be:
- ○ A carbon copy of myself
- ○ My complete opposite so that we will complement each other
- ○ Somewhat like me, but still her/his own person

Marriage is a job. Happiness or unhappiness has nothing to do with it. There was never a marriage that could not be made a success, nor a marriage that could not have ended in bitterness and failure.

—KATHLEEN NORRIS

My love life can best be described as:
- ○ Wild and footloose
- ○ Steady as she goes
- ○ A fairy tale
- ○ Sad, sad, sad
- ○ What dreams are made of
- ○ Dull and boring

I like to call my significant other, my:
- ○ Mate
- ○ Lover
- ○ Boyfriend/girlfriend
- ○ Spouse
- ○ Steady
- ○ Sweetheart

*Tip: Put more positive energy into your
relationship than you do your
career and you will live the dream
of happily ever after.*

If I marry someone from a different race, my parents would:
- ○ Accept her/him with open arms
- ○ Be concerned about some of society's views
- ○ Reject her/him
- ○ Reject us both

If I marry someone from a different religion, my parents
would:
- ○ Want to convert him/her
- ○ Not care
- ○ Want me to change my love's beliefs
- ○ Reject him/her
- ○ Reject us both

In the past, I have had trouble in relationships because I:
- ○ Feel trapped
- ○ Am afraid of rejection
- ○ Love playing the field
- ○ Get bored easily
- ○ Reveal my feelings too soon
- ○ Am too needy
- ○ Choose the wrong type of mate
- ○ Am a huge flirt

Love has the patience
To endure
The fault it sees
But cannot cure.

—EDGAR A. GUEST

After having a huge argument with my significant other, I:
- ○ Usually hold a grudge
- ○ Love to kiss and make up
- ○ Forgive and forget
- ○ Consider ending the relationship
- ○ Have a good cry
- ○ Seek solace
- ○ Sulk for a little while
- ○ Call my best friend
- ○ Go home to my mother

If one of my significant other's friends made a pass at me, I would:
- ○ Ignore it
- ○ Be flattered
- ○ Laugh it off
- ○ Tell my mate
- ○ Pursue him/her if I wanted to
- ○ Just flirt and have a little fun

Love is blind.

—*CHAUCER*

If I saw my mate flirting with someone, I'd:
- ○ Cause a huge scene
- ○ Secretly fume
- ○ Sulk, but never say how I felt
- ○ Talk about it later with my mate
- ○ Be devastated
- ○ Consider ending our relationship
- ○ Be glad that others find my mate to be attractive
- ○ Flirt with the next attractive stranger that I see

If thou wouldst marry, marry thine equal.

—*OVID*

When it comes to my personal quirks in bed, I:
- ○ Snore
- ○ Talk in my sleep
- ○ Toss and turn like a wild animal
- ○ Sleepwalk
- ○ Have frequent nightmares
- ○ Steal all the covers
- ○ Read when I can't sleep

- ○ Sleep with the light on
- ○ Eat snacks in bed
- ○ Take sleeping pills
- ○ Toss the covers on the floor during the night

When it comes to personal habits that drive my friends crazy, I:
- ○ Crack my knuckles
- ○ Talk to myself
- ○ Mutter and mumble
- ○ Am moody
- ○ Sing or whistle
- ○ Repeat myself
- ○ Exaggerate
- ○ Am a slob

Nobody tells you—stereotypical role expectations are still very prevalent in today's society.

The best way to describe my spending habits is to say that I am:
- ○ Thrifty at times, extravagant at others
- ○ Tighter than bark on a tree
- ○ Practical
- ○ Spending money faster than the speed of light
- ○ Financially savvy

To please my mate, I would be willing to:
- ○ Lose weight
- ○ Tone up my body
- ○ Color my hair

- O Change my address
- O Change my occupation
- O Have plastic surgery
- O Change my last name
- O Have children
- O Formally adopt children from a previous marriage
- O Drop a friend
- O Spend less time with my family
- O Change my spending habits
- O Change the way I dress
- O Change my grooming habits
- O Change my attitude
- O Get braces on my teeth

When it comes to saving stuff, I am:
- O The world's biggest pack rat
- O Throwing things out the door as fast as I bring them home
- O Somewhere in the middle

Tip: To have a great relationship,
pray about the relationship.

My ideal evening would consist of:
- O A very romantic date
- O Time with friends or family
- O Time alone with just my mate
- O A huge party
- O Solitude

- ○ An unusual adventure like parasailing, skydiving, or going somewhere that we have never been before
- ○ A ball-game
- ○ Hanging out at a trendy club
- ○ A society event
- ○ Time at a coffeehouse
- ○ An evening at home

The world has grown suspicious of anything that looks like a happy married life.

—OSCAR WILDE

When it comes to an evening out on the town, I usually spend:
- ○ Under $30
- ○ Between $30 and $75
- ○ Over $100, but less than $200
- ○ Over $200

My greatest fear is:
- ○ Fear of the unknown
- ○ Fear of failure
- ○ Fear of rejection
- ○ Fear of dying
- ○ Fear of being alone in the world
- ○ Fear of growing old

What's mine is yours,
And what is yours is mine.

—*SHAKESPEARE*

When I think of angels, I:
- ○ Remember when I had an encounter with one
- ○ Know that I have a guardian angel looking over me
- ○ Believe that angels help us
- ○ Think I must give them a lot of extra work just looking after my love life

The philosopher I relate to the best would be someone closest to:
- ○ Plato
- ○ Ralph Waldo Emerson
- ○ My dad

Tip: You build a happy relationship one day at a time.

I believe in life after death:
- ○ True
- ○ False

I believe that life after death consists of:
- ○ Heaven and Hell
- ○ Purgatory

- ○ Nothing
- ○ An existence very different than my current one

When it comes to the paranormal, I believe in:

- ○ Ghosts
- ○ Aliens and UFOs
- ○ ESP
- ○ Seances

My favorite time of the year is:

- ○ Spring
- ○ Summer
- ○ Autumn
- ○ Winter

When I read the morning paper, I:

- ○ Read it cover to cover
- ○ Read the headlines and any stories that appeal to me
- ○ Never talk while I read the paper
- ○ Look at only the ads—I get my news from television

Tip: Focus on the present and not on the past if you want your relationship to develop happily over time.

My favorite way to spend time alone is:

- ○ Reading
- ○ Watching TV or movies
- ○ Pampering myself
- ○ Listening to music
- ○ Playing with my animals
- ○ I don't like to spend time alone

The person that I am closest to, besides my significant other is:

- ○ My best friend
- ○ My mom
- ○ My dad
- ○ My brother
- ○ My sister
- ○ My furry, four-legged buddy
- ○ My roommate
- ○ My coworker or boss

Tip: Like your partner as much as you love him.

The people I admire most are usually:

- ○ Religious leaders
- ○ Entertainers
- ○ Sports personalities
- ○ Political leaders
- ○ Scientists
- ○ Parents
- ○ Teachers/professors
- ○ Industrialists
- ○ Authors
- ○ Artists
- ○ Movie stars

A happy marriage is a long conversation
that always seems too short.

—*ANDRÉ MAUROIS*

I believe that my best feature is:
- O   My personality
- O   My earning potential
- O   My social connections
- O   My good looks
- O   My exciting lifestyle
- O   My intelligence
- O   My spiritual wisdom
- O   My worldly treasures

My ideal marriage would be like that of:
- O   My parents'
- O   My boss's
- O   My neighbor's
- O   My friend's
- O   My sibling's

Tip: Treat your mate like a best friend and she will be.

When I get really angry, I:
- ○ Curse
- ○ Yell
- ○ Throw things
- ○ Say things that I really don't mean
- ○ Lose control
- ○ Get physically violent
- ○ Withdraw
- ○ Pout
- ○ Leave the premises

The thing that gets me most upset is:
- ○ Lovers who lie
- ○ Lovers who cheat
- ○ Lovers who withhold their affection
- ○ Lovers who take each other for granted
- ○ Lovers who talk about past loves

I see problems as:
- ○ Roadblocks
- ○ Challenges
- ○ Opportunities for growth
- ○ Just setbacks
- ○ Obstacles to my personal happiness

I feel sorry for myself:
- ○ Occasionally
- ○ Rarely
- ○ Pretty often—I have a lot going on

Man know thyself! All wisdom centers there.

—YOUNG

When I feel sorry for myself, I usually:
- ○ Cry
- ○ Whine
- ○ Complain
- ○ Withdraw
- ○ Become needy
- ○ Get defensive

Members of the opposite sex:
- ○ Intrigue me
- ○ Intimidate me
- ○ Surprise me

If I found out that my significant other was keeping a secret from me, I would:
- ○ Feel hurt
- ○ Be furious
- ○ Be intrigued and want to know more
- ○ Never trust her/him again
- ○ Feel responsible that my mate couldn't confide in me
- ○ Never tell her/him a secret

The things in my diary that I wouldn't want my significant other to read are all about:
- ○ My feelings about our relationship
- ○ My past loves

- O My current feelings for another
- O How I spend money
- O My relationships with my friends
- O My relationships with family members
- O My dreams
- O My fantasies
- O My sordid past
- O My problems at work
- O My criminal history

In lovers' quarrels, the party that loves most is always most willing to acknowledge the greater fault.

—SCOTT

I am allergic to:
- O Milk products
- O Bee stings
- O Snake bites
- O Certain medications
- O Animals
- O Dust or mold

I have had or have these physical problems:
- O Infertility problems
- O Migraines
- O Cancer
- O Chronic back pain
- O Heart trouble
- O Chemical imbalance

When you doubt, abstain.

—ZOROASTER

When I am under severe stress, the physical conditions that plague me are:
- O Heartburn
- O Hives
- O Stomach problems
- O Ulcer
- O Insomnia
- O Headaches

Love did his reason blind.
And love's the noblest frailty of the mind.

—DRYDEN

If my significant other were diagnosed with a fatal illness, I would:
- O Help in every way that I could for twenty-four hours a day
- O Fight the illness till the bitter end
- O Search the world over for a cure
- O Start to withdraw a little to protect my heart
- O Fall apart

- ○ Pray for a miracle
- ○ Break up because I just couldn't cope with it

The way that I keep my physical and mental energy level strong is to:

- ○ Pray
- ○ Meditate
- ○ Exercise regularly
- ○ Watch my diet
- ○ Get regular check ups
- ○ Go on retreats
- ○ Visit wonderful spas

I worry about:

- ○ Just about everything
- ○ My health
- ○ My children
- ○ My love life
- ○ Crime
- ○ My parents
- ○ Job security
- ○ My future in-laws
- ○ Absolutely nothing

Tip: Don't believe the old wives' tale that two can live as cheaply as one.

I believe that my mate's best feature is his/her:

- ○ Intelligence
- ○ Smile

- ○ Facial features
- ○ Toned body
- ○ Bank account
- ○ Personality
- ○ Social position

In a crisis, I am:
- ○ Calm, cool, and collected
- ○ In a state of panic
- ○ Nervous and confused
- ○ Constantly praying

The section of the newspaper that I read first is the:
- ○ Headlines
- ○ Front page
- ○ Sports
- ○ Entertainment
- ○ Classifieds
- ○ Business
- ○ Society page

I consider myself to be a:
- ○ Leader
- ○ Follower
- ○ Little bit of both

Friendship often ends in love;
but love in friendship never.

—*COLTON*

If I ran for political office my platform would include:
- ○ Tax reform
- ○ Changes in foreign policy
- ○ Changes in domestic policy
- ○ Animal rights
- ○ Human rights
- ○ Social reform

When it comes to politics, I am a:
- ○ Conservative
- ○ Liberal
- ○ Independent
- ○ Apathetic person

That you may be loved, be amiable.

—*OVID*

The reason I vote for particular political candidates is usually:
- ○ Their party affiliation
- ○ Their platform
- ○ Because my friends are backing them
- ○ Because my parents are backing them
- ○ Because my boss is backing them
- ○ Their physical appearance
- ○ I don't usually vote

If my significant other made some important choices for me, I would:
- ○ Be grateful
- ○ Feel relieved that I didn't have to

- ○ Resent it
- ○ Be shocked

My lifetime mate should be:
- ○ A genius
- ○ Intelligent
- ○ Average in intelligence
- ○ Not the brightest, but great looking
- ○ Less intelligent than me

I ask others for help:
- ○ Whenever I need any assistance at all
- ○ When I'm in a jam
- ○ Rarely

I view talking as:
- ○ A way to communicate my ideas
- ○ A way to bond with my mate
- ○ One of my favorite activities
- ○ Irritating when people just talk to be talking

Basic Relationship Savers:
Hold hands during arguments.
Kiss goodnight every single night.
Go to bed at the same time.
Say, "I love you," daily.
Hug at least three times a day.
Never go to bed angry with one another.
Always remain true to your vows.

The thing that amazes me most about people is:
- The way they waste so much of their time on insignificant matters
- How kind and wonderful human beings can be
- The cruelty in some people's hearts
- Their ability to bounce back after tragedy

At this point in my life, my priorities are:
- Religion
- My significant other
- Family
- Career
- School
- Having fun
- Friends

Ten years from now I imagine that my priorities will be:
- Religion
- Spouse
- Children
- Parents
- Career
- Keeping up with my peers
- Travel
- Building personal wealth
- Making a contribution to the world

I take time off from work:
- For a special vacation
- Because of an illness
- For mental health days
- Never—that isn't the right thing to do

When I get off from work I feel:
- ○ Tired
- ○ Emotionally drained
- ○ Ready for rest and relaxation
- ○ A bit let down—I love my job
- ○ Free and happy

When I have a business trip, I:
- ○ Will call my mate every night
- ○ Will call my mate just to say I arrived safely
- ○ Will call my mate only if an emergency arises
- ○ Don't feel the need to call at all
- ○ Will e-mail my significant other
- ○ Will fax my mate

A reserved lover, it is said,
always makes a suspicious husband.

—GOLDSMITH

If others don't take my advice, I:
- ○ Feel slighted
- ○ Think that they are foolish
- ○ Get my feelings hurt
- ○ Refuse to give my brilliant advice to them ever again
- ○ Don't really care

I like to gossip:
- ○ True
- ○ False

When it comes to listening to others talk, I:
- ○ Am an active listener
- ○ Tend to focus on what I will say next
- ○ Am a little bit spacy and allow my mind to wander

When it comes to being kind, polite, and mannerly, I am:
- ○ A saint
- ○ A pretty nice person
- ○ Sometimes a bit rude
- ○ A mother's worst nightmare

If things don't go according to my plans, I:
- ○ Get angry
- ○ Pout
- ○ Change plans
- ○ Persevere with my original plans no matter what happens
- ○ Panic

Love is a pearl of purest hue,
but stormy waves are round it;
And dearly may a woman rue,
the hour that first she found it.

—*L.E. LANDON*

A professional matchmaker would describe me as:
- ○ A diamond in the rough
- ○ A fabulous catch
- ○ In need of a major overhaul
- ○ Desperate

When it comes to self-respect, I:
- ○ Treasure myself and know that I am a worthwhile human being
- ○ Think well of myself, but could use a bit more confidence
- ○ Am a bit lacking in the self-esteem department

I tend to criticize others for:
- ○ Their attire
- ○ Their past mistakes
- ○ Their lack of manners
- ○ Their spending habits
- ○ Their career moves
- ○ Zilch—everyone should just live his/her own life

The person who upsets me the most usually is:
- ○ My mate
- ○ My ex's current mate
- ○ My ex
- ○ My child
- ○ My parent
- ○ My boss
- ○ My coworker
- ○ My mate's child
- ○ My friend

Of all mankind, each loves himself the best.

—TERENCE

When someone close to me makes a mistake, I usually:
- ○ Get angry
- ○ Get even
- ○ Try to help
- ○ Forgive him/her

On a happiness scale of one to ten, I am usually a:
- ○ Perfect ten—very happy
- ○ Seven or eight—happy
- ○ Five to six—moderately happy
- ○ Four to five—moderately unhappy
- ○ Two to three—pretty unhappy
- ○ One—major league depressed

Certain times bring up unhappy memories for me, like:
- ○ A specific season
- ○ A certain holiday
- ○ A time of day
- ○ A specific day of the year

To make others see my point of view, I:
- ○ Try to paint a word picture for them
- ○ Give them the facts and use logic to convince them
- ○ Play on their emotions
- ○ Get a bit pushy
- ○ Threaten them

I complain mostly about:
- ○ The weather
- ○ My health
- ○ The opposite sex
- ○ Money matters
- ○ My job
- ○ My family

- o My mate
- o My in-laws
- o Household chores
- o Current events

When it comes to giving compliments, I:
- o Give them freely
- o Am somewhat hesitant to give compliments
- o View them as flattery and therefore don't give any

In the morning, while I am getting dressed and eating breakfast, I think about:
- o Work
- o God
- o The day ahead
- o My four-legged buddy
- o My children
- o My significant other
- o Sex

Tip: Take your time and deeply examine your relationship. True love will wait.

I view flirting as:
- o Prolonged eye contact with a member of the opposite sex
- o Touching
- o Complimenting
- o Teasing
- o Sexual innuendos

The most popular strategies for remaining compatible:
Be trustworthy and kind at all times.
Talk openly and honestly with each other about everything.
Always treat each other with respect and kindness.
Give each other room to grow.
Have a spiritual foundation for the relationship.

When it comes to flirting with those other than my mate, I:
- ○ Can flirt with the best of them
- ○ View flirting as harmless fun
- ○ Think it enhances my romantic side
- ○ Only flirt with my significant other

After the honeymoon is over, I expect to have sex with my mate:
- ○ Once a week
- ○ Two to three times a week
- ○ Daily
- ○ Once a month
- ○ Once in a blue moon

The meeting of two personalities is like the contact of two chemical substances; if there is any reaction, both are transformed.

—CARL JUNG

I believe that "little white lies" are:

- ○ Just a part of being tactful
- ○ Ways to save other's feelings
- ○ A coward's way out
- ○ Wrong, no matter what the circumstance might be

If I had a complaint about my significant other's friends, it would be that:

- ○ They smoke
- ○ They drink too much
- ○ They dress in an unacceptable manner
- ○ They use foul language or bad grammar
- ○ They aren't likable in my book
- ○ They have made poor career choices
- ○ They are sloppy
- ○ They are disrespectful to my gender
- ○ They don't like me
- ○ They ignore me or my feelings
- ○ They are sports nuts

I spend most of my time with my:

- ○ Significant other
- ○ Friends

- o Coworkers
- o Pets
- o Siblings
- o Roommates
- o Neighbors

The most difficult thing in life is to know yourself.
—*THALES*

Some of my friends are:
- o From another planet
- o Of a different race
- o Homosexual
- o Members of a different religion
- o Much younger than I
- o Much older than I

I like to write letters to:
- o My significant other
- o Pen pals
- o Ex-loves
- o Relatives
- o Friends in faraway places

The only phone calls that I return are:
- o Work-related calls that I just have to return
- o From important people only
- o From my parents
- o From my mate

○ Few and far between
○ From close friends

If I won the lottery, I'd:
○ Quit my job in a heartbeat
○ Take a dream vacation
○ Help out my favorite charity
○ Give money to my parents
○ Invest most of it
○ Shop till I drop
○ Buy a new house

Nobody tells you—people are on their best behavior before they get married and that behavior will change after marriage.

Everyday events that give me the "willies" are:
○ Public speaking
○ Flying
○ Storms
○ Driving in snow
○ Being alone late at night
○ Meeting new people

> *The best romance enhancers:*
> *Soft music*
> *Candles*
> *Fresh flowers*
> *Gourmet foods*
> *Romantic attitude*

When it comes to jealousy, I:
- ○ Am a green-eyed monster
- ○ Don't have a jealous bone in my body
- ○ Only get jealous on very rare occasions

I plan to move to a new city within the next:
- ○ Six-months to a year
- ○ Five years
- ○ Never—this is home

> *Love is not blind—it sees more, not less. But because it sees more, it is willing to see less.*
>
> —*Rabbi Julius Gordon*

My ideal place of residence would be:
- ○ A major city—so much to do and see
- ○ A quiet little town where everyone knows my name

- ○ A midsize city that offers the best of both worlds
- ○ The country

If my mate got a promotion out of town, I would:
- ○ Move to be with her/him
- ○ Wish her/him well, but stay behind
- ○ Be open for discussion
- ○ Would expect her/him to stay with me
- ○ Have a commuter marriage

Nobody tells you—the romance factor will often lessen after getting married.

I plan to change occupations:
- ○ Often—I like variety
- ○ Only when the need arises
- ○ Whenever I can boost my career
- ○ Never

If I could live my life like a movie script, it would be a:
- ○ Love story
- ○ Drama
- ○ Comedy
- ○ Thriller
- ○ Blockbuster with lots of action
- ○ Foreign film
- ○ Mystery

Money, you know, will hide many faults.
—*CERVANTES*

If I had a will, I would leave all of my money to:
- ○ My significant other
- ○ My parents
- ○ A trust fund set up to take care of my pets
- ○ My siblings
- ○ My favorite charity

Tip: The best way to end an argument
is to kiss and make up.

When I am running late, I:
- ○ Call to explain
- ○ Hurry and rush
- ○ Panic
- ○ Don't worry about it
- ○ Get grumpy and cranky

When I am with my friends, I:
- ○ Like to include my mate
- ○ Enjoy just being out with my pals
- ○ Like some time with my friends without my mate and some time with my friends that includes my mate

The five most popular dates are:
Dinner at a restaurant.
Movies/Rental movies.
Concerts.
Parties or weddings.
Time spent with friends.

My little bedtime idiosyncrasies include:
- ○ Sleeping with a stuffed toy
- ○ Sleeping with my four-legged buddy
- ○ Sleeping under a zillion covers
- ○ Drinking warm milk
- ○ Sleeping in unusual pj's
- ○ Calling friends or family before going to sleep

Want to know if your significant other is right for you?
Just ask yourself if he improves the overall quality of
your life.

The main way that I save money is to:
- ○ Live well below my means
- ○ Cut back in specific areas of my life
- ○ Buy stocks or bonds
- ○ Use coupons

- ○ Shop sales
- ○ Put money in the bank
- ○ Put money in my 401(k) at work

Familiarity breeds contempt.

—Aesop

I need this amount of income to cover my living expenses for a year:

- ○ Under $15,000
- ○ Under $35,000
- ○ Under $50,000
- ○ Under $75,000
- ○ Under $100,000
- ○ Under $200,000
- ○ More than $200,000

This year, I expect to earn:

- ○ Under $20,000
- ○ Between $20,000 and $35,000
- ○ Between $35,000 and $50,000
- ○ Between $50,000 and $75,000
- ○ Between $75,000 and $100,000
- ○ Between $100,000 and $150,000
- ○ Between $150,000 and $200,000
- ○ Over $200,000

Five years from now, I expect to be earning:

- ○ The same amount that I am currently earning

- ○ A salary in keeping with the increase in the cost of living
- ○ Considerably more than I am now

I plan to continue the career path that I am on now, for:
- ○ A year or two
- ○ Forever
- ○ I really don't know

Tip: If you want to stay happily married, remain true to your wedding vows.

I believe that I:
- ○ Must make my own way in the world
- ○ Can expect financial help from my family
- ○ Will one day win the lottery if I play often enough
- ○ Will be supported by my spouse
- ○ Can expect financial help from my mate's family

When it comes to paying bills, I:
- ○ Pay them as soon as I receive them
- ○ Pay only the most urgent ones and then wait till I have more money to pay the remaining ones
- ○ Pay all my bills at the end of each month

Nobody tells you—couples often fall into the same style of marriage that their parents had.

I believe that I will share all of my worldly goods with my mate except:
- ○ My inheritance from my family
- ○ My savings prior to marriage
- ○ My valuable collectibles
- ○ My electronic equipment
- ○ My clothing
- ○ My beloved car
- ○ No exceptions, we will share everything

When it comes to luxury items, my top priorities are:
- ○ Trips to exotic locations
- ○ Cars
- ○ Fine jewelry
- ○ Art
- ○ A vacation home
- ○ Fine wines
- ○ Designer clothing
- ○ Antiques

They do not love that do not show their love.

—SHAKESPEARE

My hobbies cost annually:
- ○ Under $200
- ○ Under $500
- ○ Between $500 and $1000
- ○ Between $1000 and $5000
- ○ Between $5000 and $10,000
- ○ Over $10,000

Each month, I spend this amount on personal grooming:
- ○ Under $25
- ○ About $50
- ○ Close to $100
- ○ Near $200
- ○ Over $250

Tip: Look for a mate who is emotionally open, growing, and available.

I believe in:
- ○ Not saving money, but living for today
- ○ Saving 5 percent to 10 percent of my income
- ○ Saving as much as I possibly can

When I save money, I like to put it in:
- ○ A bank
- ○ Stocks and bonds
- ○ Real estate or other investments
- ○ My piggybank
- ○ I never have money to save

Tip: If you want to have romance in your love life, act like a romantic lover would act.

The majority of my disposable income is spent on:
- ○ Travel
- ○ Entertainment
- ○ Clothing
- ○ Home furnishings
- ○ Jewelry
- ○ Status symbols
- ○ My pets
- ○ Charities

My philosophy about money is best summed up as:
- ○ Wealth belongs not to those who have it,
  but to those who enjoy it
- ○ Saved money is earned money

Nobody tells you—
a good marriage takes lots of hard work.

When it comes to using credit cards, I:
- ○ Use them, love them—credit is my lifestyle
- ○ Think of them only as a convenience and I pay the
  full balance at the end of each month
- ○ Use them, but my monthly payments are quite
  reasonable
- ○ Need credit counseling and soon!

When it comes to buying things, I:
- ○ Always pay the full retail price
- ○ Shop sales
- ○ Shop flea markets and garage sales

- ○ Shop retail outlets
- ○ Order everything by mail
- ○ Put things in layaway
- ○ Like to haggle over all purchases

Where there's marriage without love,
there will be love without marriage.

—*BEN FRANKLIN*

When I go grocery shopping, I:
- ○ Always have a list
- ○ Have my budget clearly in my mind
- ○ Buy whatever strikes my fancy
- ○ Hurry through the shopping to get it over—I dislike it a ton
- ○ Meander through the aisles looking for yummy new items
- ○ Sample different foods throughout the store

I buy most of my groceries at a:
- ○ Farmer's market
- ○ Supermarket
- ○ Wholesale club
- ○ Convenience store

The way I decide to choose what I am having for dinner is to:
- ○ Look in the cupboards
- ○ Follow my weekly meal plan
- ○ Phone a restaurant for dinner reservations
- ○ Drive through a fast-food restaurant for take-out

- ○ Call my mom to have me over for dinner
- ○ Invite my friends over for a pot luck meal and hope for the best

My weight is usually:
- ○ Constant—what you see is what you get
- ○ Always changing—if you don't like me today just stick around as I will look different in the near future

---

Tip: One of the biggest predictors of whether a marriage will stand the test of time is the degree of commitment that each partner feels.

I plan to be involved in my community by:
- ○ Giving to my favorite charity
- ○ Working at my church
- ○ Becoming involved in politics
- ○ Saving the environment
- ○ Becoming a mentor to a child
- ○ Feeding the poor

Great dates to help keep the fun times happening:
Dinner and dancing
Ballooning
Moonlight picnics
Concerts
Shows
Cooking a gourmet meal together
Holiday events
Sailing
First-rate sports events
Theme park visits
Stargazing and soul-searching
Dog shows
Country picnics
Exploring your city like tourists
Taking a class together

When I am sick, I:
- ○ Want to be pampered and taken care of by my significant other
- ○ Need to be left alone
- ○ Turn into the world's crankiest person
- ○ Get scared and think the worst
- ○ Call my mother
- ○ Whine and complain
- ○ Act like a big baby

True love is like ghosts, which everybody talks about and few have seen.

—LA ROCHEFOUCAULD

I think you should go to the doctor:
- O Every time that you get sick
- O Only after you try to self-medicate
- O When you are very ill
- O Only in emergencies

When it comes to gambling, I:
- O Have never gambled
- O Play the lottery
- O Go to the riverboats to gamble
- O Like to vacation in a city that has many casinos
- O Believe that gambling is morally wrong
- O Have a gambling problem
- O Play bingo for money
- O Play cards for money

Tip: If you want to be happy with your mate, concentrate on your similarities, not the differences that cause you unhappiness.

I have or want to have memberships to the following types of clubs:
- ○ Athletic club
- ○ Country club
- ○ Health club
- ○ Dinner club
- ○ Social club

Know thyself.

—*ANONYMOUS*

When it comes to pets, I prefer:
- ○ Dogs
- ○ Cats
- ○ Rabbits
- ○ Fish
- ○ Other—specify
- ○ I am not an animal lover

I think of my pet as:
- ○ Part of the family
- ○ A first-rate friend and confidant
- ○ A substitute child
- ○ Just a nice, furry creature

Ways to fight a fair fight:
Pick a good time to talk to your mate.
Limit the conversation to only one topic.
Remain calm.
Listen to what your mate has to say.
Calmly tell your point of view.
Put yourself in your mate's shoes.
Be fair and reasonable.

I allow my pet to:
- ○ Sleep on my bed
- ○ Go everywhere in my home
- ○ Eat at the table
- ○ Sit on the furniture

Tip: Brainstorm to come up with hobbies, activities and interests that the two of you can share together to keep your relationship strong and vital.

The kinds of dogs that I like the best are:
- ○ Big, active breeds like Goldens and Bernese mountain dogs
- ○ Tiny, toy breeds like a Yorkie

○ A lovable mutt from the pound
○ A guard dog like a Doberman
○ Mid-size dogs like a cocker spaniel
○ Any and all dogs—I'm a dog lover

During most conversations, I talk about _____ of the time:
○ Ten percent
○ Twenty-five percent
○ About fifty percent
○ About seventy-five percent
○ Way too much!

My body language is generally:
○ Proper and formal
○ Fidgety
○ Relaxed
○ Tense

Free and fair discussion will ever be found the firmest friend to truth.

—GEORGE CAMPBELL

When it comes to smiling, I:
○ Smile a bunch
○ Smile only when I am extremely happy
○ Hate my teeth and try never to smile
○ See it as a show of weakness
○ Wish I smiled more often

If I get stuck in traffic, I:
- ○ Go crazy
- ○ Feel mildly irritated
- ○ Kick back and make the best of it

If I get lost, I:
- ○ Ask for directions
- ○ Get out a map
- ○ Keep on looking
- ○ Panic

When driving, I_____ run out of gas:
- ○ Have never
- ○ Rarely
- ○ Often

When something breaks and it needs to be fixed, I usually:
- ○ Try to repair it myself
- ○ Call a professional
- ○ Ask a friend or relative for help

I change the oil in my car:
- ○ Every three-thousand miles
- ○ Every five-thousand miles
- ○ Whenever

The definition of tacky to me is:
- ○ Yard ornaments
- ○ Hot rods
- ○ Curlers worn in public
- ○ T-shirts with crass statements
- ○ Spending money to impress others

Keeping up with my neighbors, friends, or coworkers is:
- ○ Very important to me
- ○ Somewhat important to me
- ○ Doesn't matter to me

Tip: If you want to be truly happy in your relationship, think cooperation instead of competition.

If I could only have one of the following, it would be:
- ○ Great wealth
- ○ Vast knowledge
- ○ Exciting sex
- ○ True friends
- ○ Much fame
- ○ Long life
- ○ Perfect health
- ○ One loyal dog
- ○ True romance

When it comes to snooping, I might admit to:
- ○ Reading someone else's diary
- ○ Eavesdropping on a telephone call
- ○ Listening at the door to a conversation
- ○ Looking through a coworker's desk
- ○ Going through my mate's wallet/purse
- ○ Following someone to see where she goes

Please don't tell anyone, but when I was little, I:
- ○ Was scared of the dark
- ○ Was a bed wetter
- ○ Ran away from home
- ○ Got into some serious trouble
- ○ Was expelled from school

Most of my comedic comments are:
- ○ Sarcastic
- ○ Based on my observations of the world
- ○ Tried and true jokes
- ○ Kid's riddles
- ○ Put-downs directed at my friends or mate

I believe certain subjects should not be discussed during meals, like:
- ○ Our sex life
- ○ Religious differences
- ○ Past love affairs
- ○ Skeletons in the closet
- ○ Past mistakes

The wound's invisible
That love's keen arrows make.

—*SHAKESPEARE*

The most difficult part of my life is my:
- ○ Career
- ○ Relationship with my parents
- ○ Relationship with my children
- ○ Love life
- ○ Financial situation
- ○ Health
- ○ Social life

My friends call me superstitious because I:
- ○ Am scared on Friday the 13th
- ○ Won't walk under a ladder
- ○ Cross my fingers for good luck
- ○ Have lucky numbers
- ○ Have a lucky charm
- ○ Wear a lucky garment

For me to comment on my significant other's weight, he/she would have to:
- ○ Ask me for an opinion
- ○ Have gained at least five pounds
- ○ Have gained at least ten pounds
- ○ Have lost weight

I consider myself to be a:
- ○ Take-charge person
- ○ Pushover
- ○ Sometimes tough and sometimes a softy
- ○ Middle-of-the-road type of person

The last three books that I read were:
- ○ Fiction
- ○ Nonfiction
- ○ Self-help
- ○ Inspirational
- ○ Religious
- ○ Financial
- ○ Work-related topics
- ○ Poetry
- ○ Great literature
- ○ Best-sellers
- ○ Mysteries
- ○ Who has time to read?

My clothes are mostly:
- ○ Custom made
- ○ Designer labels
- ○ Bought off the rack
- ○ Hand-me-downs
- ○ Garage sale finds

I check my appearance in a mirror:
- ○ When I get dressed
- ○ Whenever I go out of the house
- ○ Hardly ever
- ○ Frequently throughout the day

I am against hunting because:
- ○ It is cruel and inhumane
- ○ People can get hurt
- ○ People shouldn't own guns
- ○ I don't want animals to suffer
- ○ I go hunting

*Tip: A good relationship takes
self-restraint and self-love.*

I believe that people should be vegetarians:
- ○ True
- ○ False

I believe that people should not wear furs:
- ○ True
- ○ False

I feel that men and women should be paid the same set of wages for doing the same job:
- ○ True
- ○ False

During an average week, I expect to be out with my friends:
- ○ One night a week
- ○ A couple of nights per week
- ○ Most evenings
- ○ A night out with friends is a rarity for me

Keep your eyes wide open before marriage,
and half-shut afterwards.

—BEN FRANKLIN

Speaking of friends, I:
- ○ Have zillions of friends
- ○ Have a midsize group of pals
- ○ Have a couple of close friends
- ○ Have a best buddy
- ○ Am known as a loner

Don't marry for money; you can borrow it cheaper.

—SCOTCH PROVERB

I talk on the telephone to my friends or family:
- Only when an occasion warrants
- Under thirty minutes a day
- About an hour a day
- Two hours or less
- All the time—I have a phone growing out of the side of my head

I use e-mail:
- Just for work-related communications
- To keep in touch with my family
- To keep in touch with friends
- To touch base with my mate

When I make a guest list for a party, I:
- Invite only the closest of friends
- Pick and choose just the right blend of interesting acquaintances
- Like to make it a family affair
- Include neighbors
- Want to invite people who could help my social standing
- Include professional acquaintances
- Always include my coworkers
- Invite just about everyone in the world!

If you love, you are welcome in the universe;
if you are loved, you are at home here.

—*FRANK PITTMAN, M.D.*

My social life can best be described as:
- ○ I am a hermit
- ○ I'm a party animal
- ○ I am a magnet for friends
- ○ I just like to be alone with my mate

In public, I prefer to:
- ○ Be the center of attention
- ○ Blend into the crowd
- ○ Have my mate by my side
- ○ Be seen as a role model for the perfect mate

Nobody tells you—old flames don't make for good friends if you want to be happy with your current flame.

When it comes to my siblings, they are:
- ○ My closest friends
- ○ Bad news
- ○ Nuisances
- ○ Practically strangers to me
- ○ My worst nightmare

People tell me that I am most like:
- ○ My mother
- ○ My dad
- ○ A sibling

- O   My significant other
- O   My closest friend
- O   A specific famous person—specify

As many as there are marriages, so are there many different living arrangements.

—*ANONYMOUS*

When it comes to new activities, I:
- O   Am open, willing and able to try them
- O   Am the king of caution
- O   Never like to try new things, but I will to please my mate

I require:
- O   Eight hours of sleep per night
- O   Less than six hours of sleep a night
- O   I'm a bear and could sleep for an entire winter

The most common topics of arguments:
Leisure-time activities
Friends
Household chores
Children
Sex
In-laws
Savings
Flirting with others
Ex-loves
Personal grooming habits
Holiday plans
How to spend disposable income

When it comes to watching television, I:
- ○ Never have time to watch TV
- ○ Watch many hours of television
- ○ Have a couple of programs that I wouldn't miss, but other than those, I'm not glued to the tube
- ○ Only watch sports
- ○ Can take it or leave it
- ○ Like only the news programs
- ○ Enjoy the noise of it in the background
- ○ Watch it only to learn about the world around me

Loving requires autonomy and is based on the ability to share one's self with another out of choice, as opposed to dependent need.

—*AARON STERN*

When it comes to celebrating holidays, I like to:
- O Give gifts
- O Throw parties
- O Decorate my home
- O Send cards
- O Travel
- O Spend time with my family

I celebrate all holidays, except:
- O Those of religions other than my own
- O Those that conflict with my work schedule
- O Those of other countries
- O Those that happen when I am not in a relationship

When it comes to planning my golden years, I want to:
- O Retire and take life easy
- O Travel the world
- O Spend time with my children
- O Spend time with my grandchildren
- O Start a new career
- O Honeymoon all over again with my lifetime mate
- O Work for my favorite charity
- O Fish

- ○ Play golf all day long
- ○ Move to a warmer climate
- ○ Get an RV and hit the road

Tip: The best reason to get married is for true love.

New Year's Eve should be a time for:
- ○ Reflection and making resolutions
- ○ Romantic celebrations for two
- ○ New Beginnings
- ○ A huge party
- ○ Family and friends to get together

When it comes to my mate giving me gifts, I want my mate to be:
- ○ Extravagant
- ○ Practical
- ○ Thoughtful and to buy me the gift that I have been hinting about
- ○ Carefree about gifts like me—I don't really care about material things
- ○ Giving a homemade present because those are the ones that mean the most to me
- ○ Shopping for presents all year long
- ○ Always giving me gifts

Nobody tells you—all relationships change after a couple ties the knot, so just make sure that the changes are positive ones.

I spend _____ hours on the internet each month:
- ○ A couple
- ○ Several
- ○ About ten
- ○ More than fifteen

My favorite sports are:
- ○ Football
- ○ Baseball
- ○ Basketball
- ○ Tennis
- ○ Soccer
- ○ Bowling
- ○ Swimming
- ○ Hiking
- ○ Racquetball
- ○ Golf
- ○ Sailing
- ○ I don't really care for sports

The room where I spend most of my time is the:
- ○ Bedroom
- ○ Bathroom
- ○ Kitchen
- ○ Den or home office
- ○ Living room

My desk looks like:

- ○ It was hit by a tornado
- ○ A picture of organization
- ○ It belongs to someone who works very hard
- ○ Who needs a desk?

Let there be space in your togetherness.

—*KAHLIL GIBRAN*

My personal style can best be described as:

- ○ Formal and elegant
- ○ Casual but stylish
- ○ Big kid chic
- ○ Trendy
- ○ Very, very relaxed—some might say that I don't really have any style

Tip: Praise your mate in public,
but criticize in private.

I would love for my dream home to be:

- ○ An estate
- ○ A farm
- ○ A cabin in the woods
- ○ A historic home

- ○ A trendy townhouse
- ○ A house with a white picket fence
- ○ A nice mobile home
- ○ A condo
- ○ Anywhere with the "correct" address
- ○ Any home with a pool
- ○ An apartment, who wants to take care of a house?

The style of home decor that best suits me is:
- ○ Modern or contemporary
- ○ English country
- ○ Country French
- ○ American country
- ○ Traditional
- ○ Eclectic
- ○ I just don't care about interior design

Compliments = Marriage Fuel

The worldly goods that mean the most to me are:
- ○ Photo albums
- ○ Jewelry
- ○ Antiques
- ○ Childhood mementos
- ○ My collections
- ○ Family heirlooms
- ○ My clothes
- ○ I don't really care about possessions

When I am at home alone, I usually have:

- ○ The television on
- ○ The radio playing in the background
- ○ The stereo playing full blast
- ○ Total peace and quiet

I would like my home to be decorated in:

- ○ Shades of blue and green
- ○ Warm earth tones
- ○ Calming, neutral tones
- ○ Vibrant colors that give life to the home
- ○ Many different colors, as I like variety

Ways to tell if it is true love:
You want the best for your significant other.
The future seems better with your mate
as a big part of it.
You feel in your heart of hearts that
it is truly love, not infatuation.
The relationship has lasted more
than a few weeks or months.
Your partner increases your self-esteem.
You want the relationship to last forever.
Your significant other is someone you trust.
Your significant other is someone you respect.
You don't need each other, but you want to be together.
The relationship enhances the quality of your life.

When I am not at work, I dress:
- ○ Like a bum—nobody from the office would even recognize me
- ○ Like a fashion model
- ○ In a totally different style than at the office
- ○ Pretty much the same as at the office

Nobody tells you—your choice of mate will have far-reaching consequences. It is serious business to pick a partner.

My favorite television programs are generally:
- ○ Comedies
- ○ Dramas
- ○ Sports
- ○ News reports
- ○ Talk shows
- ○ Game shows
- ○ Movies

When it comes to being up on current events, I could:
- ○ Produce a news program as, I know so much
- ○ Write the headlines, as I always have a general idea about what is taking place in the world
- ○ Fake my way through a brief conversation, at best
- ○ Not care less

Nobody tells you—women like to talk about relationship issues more than men do.

I clean my house:
- ○ By hiring a maid
- ○ Only when company is coming
- ○ Daily, my house is spotless
- ○ Weekly
- ○ Never, the health department is coming to visit me soon!

When I get good news, I:
- ○ Keep it to myself
- ○ Call my significant other
- ○ Call my friends
- ○ Tell my family
- ○ Tell my coworkers
- ○ Go into shock: I never get good news!

My favorite type of party is:
- ○ A backyard barbecue
- ○ A formal dinner party
- ○ A large cocktail party
- ○ A small informal gathering of close friends
- ○ A huge blowout with tons of people
- ○ I don't really like parties

*Tip: If you want to find a good mate,
first, be a good mate.*

I like to celebrate my birthday with:
- ○ A birthday cake
- ○ Presents
- ○ Party
- ○ Romantic birthday dinner
- ○ Family celebration
- ○ My closest friends
- ○ Cards
- ○ I don't really like birthdays

*Tip: The best romances take place
between two equal partners.*

When I buy a home, my main area of interest is:
- ○ Location
- ○ Exterior style
- ○ Interior style
- ○ The price
- ○ Proximity to work
- ○ Good school district
- ○ Proximity to family/friends
- ○ The neighbors
- ○ An address with status

Nothing is more powerful than habit.

—OVID

I believe that men and women are:
- ○ Extremely different
- ○ Mostly alike
- ○ From two different planets
- ○ Created equal
- ○ Men are superior
- ○ Women are superior

I think rainy days were made for:
- ○ Giving me the blues
- ○ Curling up on the couch with a good book
- ○ Lovers to stay home and snuggle
- ○ Ruining the day

A successful marriage is an edifice
that must be rebuilt every day.

—ANDRÉ MAUROIS

My general health can best be described as:
- ○ I'm the picture of the perfect human specimen
- ○ I'm a disease magnet
- ○ I'm very typical of the average person

When it comes to watching my weight, I:
- ○ Count every calorie
- ○ Can eat whatever I want and not gain weight
- ○ Gain weight by just looking at food
- ○ Simply don't care

When it comes to driving, I:
- ○ Could be a race car driver
- ○ Am usually passed by little old ladies
- ○ Go with the flow
- ○ Hate to drive
- ○ Love to drive just for the sake of driving

Familiar acts are made beautiful through love.

—SHELLEY

I spend most of my pocket change on:
- ○ Junk
- ○ Snacks/drinks
- ○ Magazines
- ○ I don't have a clue where my money goes
- ○ I save it
- ○ I never have change

When it comes to little gestures of love, I:
- ○ Love to snuggle
- ○ Give hugs
- ○ Kiss often
- ○ Hold my mate's hand

- ○ Walk arm in arm
- ○ Want to give/receive small gifts
- ○ Want to give/receive compliments

---

*Tip: A hug and kiss a day keep the
divorce attorney away.*

When I watch television, I:
- ○ Channel surf
- ○ Am glued to the tube
- ○ Always other stuff at the same time

---

*Nobody tells you—even in the best of relationships,
there are difficult times.*

The best way to describe the condition of my car is:
- ○ Immaculate
- ○ Just a bit run-down
- ○ A pigpen
- ○ Okay, but I'd have to clean it if my boss needed to ride in it

The type of car I own or plan to own is a:
- ○ Luxury sedan
- ○ Mini van
- ○ Truck
- ○ Jeep

- ○ Compact model
- ○ Midsize model
- ○ Sports car
- ○ Convertible

---

*Tip: Spend more time with your mate
than you do with your friends.*

When it comes to owning/buying a car, I:
- ○ Lease
- ○ Buy the car outright
- ○ Pay for the car over a period of time
- ○ Buy a used vehicle

---

*Success in love consists not so much in marrying the
one person who can make you happy as in escaping the
many who could make you miserable.*

—ANONYMOUS

By the way I keep house, my friends call me:
- ○ A perfectionist
- ○ A slob
- ○ A born housekeeper
- ○ A mother's worst nightmare
- ○ An ad for the health department

Great occasions for a couple to celebrate:
First date
First kiss
Moment that you each feel in love
First fight and makeup
Engagement anniversary
Wedding day
Anniversaries

When it comes to giving advice, I:
- ○ Give it freely to anyone who will listen
- ○ Believe that, "Wise men don't need it, fools won't heed it"
- ○ Only give it when it is requested

When I attend a party, I:
- ○ Am the first to arrive
- ○ Stay late
- ○ Am the life of it
- ○ Make an appearance and leave
- ○ Want to spend the entire time with my mate
- ○ Love to mingle
- ○ Like to flirt with others
- ○ Never go to parties

Married in haste, repent in leisure.
—WILLIAM CONGREVE

When I think about choosing an apartment or condo, I would like:
- ○ A terrific location
- ○ Spacious rooms
- ○ Lots of storage
- ○ Tennis courts
- ○ A swimming pool
- ○ Community party house

When it comes to spending money on entertainment, I:
- ○ Spend less than 10 percent of my income on it
- ○ Have a budget and stick to it
- ○ Spend whatever I want, so that I can enjoy life to the fullest

If I would decide to go back to school for another degree, I plan to finance it by:
- ○ Dipping into my savings
- ○ Getting a student loan
- ○ Having my employer pay for it
- ○ Asking my parents to help pay for it
- ○ Asking my spouse to pay for it

Important milestones in the life of a couple:
First meeting
Falling in love
Becoming serious
Meeting each other's friends
Surviving your first big fight
Getting engaged
Meeting each other's family
The wedding
Buying your first home
Getting a beloved pet
Having children
Important anniversaries
Having grandchildren

When it comes to my personality, I am best described as:

- O Easygoing
- O Sensitive
- O Excitable
- O Moody
- O Unemotional—I'm a human robot

I like to argue my point of view:

- O True
- O False

I am rarely wrong or make a mistake:
- o   True
- o   False

On Saturday mornings, I usually:
- o   Stay in bed to catch up on my sleep
- o   Get up early to spend time with family or friends
- o   Run errands
- o   Lounge around the house
- o   Do household chores
- o   Head to the office
- o   Head to the nearest park with my dog
- o   Play sports
- o   Shop till I drop

Nobody tells you—your partner's friends, family, and career will greatly impact your own life once you are married.

When it comes to "natural beauty," I:
- o   Have to admit I color my hair
- o   Wear fake fingernails
- o   Wear false eyelashes
- o   Spend time at tanning salons
- o   Spend hours putting on my makeup
- o   Have had cosmetic surgery
- o   Wear a retainer at night

*Tip: To be happy in your romantic relationship,
maintain a full life outside of it.*

When it comes to exercising, I:
- ○ Don't exercise at all
- ○ Jog regularly
- ○ Walk
- ○ Play sports
- ○ Belong to a health club

*Marriage, to women as to men, must be a luxury,
not a necessity: an incident of life, not all of it.*

—SUSAN B. ANTHONY

My favorite type of music is:
- ○ Rock
- ○ Country
- ○ Classical
- ○ Gospel
- ○ Jazz

When it comes to vacations, I prefer:
- ○ Rest and relaxation
- ○ Travel to an exotic location

- ○ An adventure
- ○ Visiting a theme park
- ○ Health spa pampering
- ○ A working experience
- ○ Catching up on chores at home
- ○ Visiting relatives
- ○ Doing mission work for my church
- ○ A romantic getaway for two

One word frees us of all the weight and pain of life:
That word is love.

—SOPHOCLES

When it comes to romance, I'm:
- ○ The most romantic person in the world—Cupid calls me for tips
- ○ Average
- ○ Unromantic and proud of it
- ○ Sure that romance is overrated

A typical Saturday afternoon for me consists of:
- ○ Errands
- ○ Chores
- ○ Shopping
- ○ Museums
- ○ Time with friends
- ○ Movies
- ○ Sports

- ○ Work
- ○ Sightseeing
- ○ Romance
- ○ Time with my pets

Love is the only way to grasp another human being in the innermost core of his personality.

—VIKTOR FRANKL

When I get dressed, I usually:
- ○ Dress to impress members of the opposite sex
- ○ Use clothes as status symbols
- ○ Try hard to dress to please my mate
- ○ Look like a page from a fashion magazine
- ○ Throw on the first thing I see

When it comes to clothing, I prefer:
- ○ To spend a small fortune on them for I believe that clothes make the person
- ○ To shop sales and try to look good on a small budget
- ○ To buy just the basics because I don't really care about my wardrobe

Great romantic gift ideas:
Pearls
Perfume
Gold cuff links
Sterling silver picture frames
Concert tickets
A diamond ring
Gold jewelry
Antiques
Fine art

When it comes to fine jewelry, I:
- ❍ Have to have the basics—a gold watch, a wedding band, and a lovely engagement ring
- ❍ Believe that spending money for jewelry is frivolous
- ❍ Want more than the Queen of England owns

Nobody tells you—she will call her mother and friends more than you could ever imagine.

My favorite piece of clothing is a:
- ❍ Pair of old jeans
- ❍ Cashmere sweater
- ❍ Team jersey

○ Designer suit/outfit
○ Homemade garment

People wouldn't get divorced for such trivial reasons, if they didn't get married for such trivial reasons.

—ANONYMOUS

My parents expect me and my mate to come over to their home:
○ Weekly
○ Once or twice a month
○ Only on holidays
○ All of the time
○ Never—they like having an empty nest

When it comes to shoes, I:
○ Only buy designer shoes
○ Love tennis shoes and wear them almost everywhere
○ Own a zillion pairs
○ Go stocking-footed whenever I can
○ Buy only practical styles
○ Love to go barefoot

I plan to entertain my parents:
○ Weekly
○ On major holidays
○ Once or twice a month
○ Never
○ All of the time

On my birthday, my parents usually:
- ○ Call me
- ○ Come by my house for a visit
- ○ Take me out to eat
- ○ Give me a birthday present
- ○ Bake me a cake
- ○ Throw a family get-together for me
- ○ Send a card
- ○ Forget my big day

On my parents' anniversary, I usually:
- ○ Send a card
- ○ Call them
- ○ Give them a gift
- ○ Invite them over for dinner
- ○ Ignore it

The family member that I feel closest to is my:
- ○ Sister
- ○ Brother
- ○ Mom
- ○ Child
- ○ Stepparent
- ○ Aunt
- ○ Dad
- ○ Uncle
- ○ Grandmother
- ○ Grandfather

My friends would say that I:
- ○ Have a great relationship with my parents
- ○ Am too close to my parents
- ○ Should get closer to my folks

Growing up, I lived:
- ○ With my biological parents
- ○ In foster care
- ○ In an orphanage
- ○ With my dad
- ○ With my mom
- ○ With my grandparents
- ○ With a family friend
- ○ With my stepfamily

If you do not tell the truth about yourself,
you cannot tell it about other people.

—*VIRGINIA WOOLF*

My parents are:
- ○ Unsung heroes
- ○ Overprotective of me
- ○ Two of my best friends
- ○ Major pains in the neck
- ○ Always butting into my business
- ○ Crazy about my last significant other
- ○ Hoping that I get married
- ○ Anxious to become grandparents

My mother calls me:
- ○ Daily
- ○ Weekly
- ○ Monthly
- ○ All of the time
- ○ Never

The most popular requirements of
honeymoon destinations:
Romantic setting
Nice accommodations
Fine dining
Leisure-time activities
Privacy

When I think about my future in-laws, I:
- ○ Get excited—what terrific people!
- ○ Cringe with fear
- ○ Feel a twinge of stress
- ○ Wonder how these people could have such a wonderful child

Family gatherings in my family usually last:
- ○ One to two hours
- ○ Under four hours
- ○ Five hours
- ○ All day or all evening

Home is the place where when you go there,
they have to take you in.
—ROBERT FROST

My out-of-town family members usually visit me:
- ○ Annually
- ○ Twice a year
- ○ Three to four times a year
- ○ Monthly
- ○ All the time—I practically run a hotel for my family

On an average day, I expect to eat the following meals with my mate:
- ○ Breakfast
- ○ Lunch
- ○ Dinner

During an average weekend, I expect to eat the following meals with my mate:
- ○ Saturday breakfast
- ○ Saturday lunch
- ○ Saturday dinner
- ○ Breakfast on Sunday
- ○ Sunday lunch/brunch
- ○ Sunday dinner/supper

A typical Sunday for me consists of:
- ○ Church
- ○ Errands
- ○ Chores
- ○ Rest and relaxation
- ○ Time with friends
- ○ Time with family
- ○ Sleeping in late
- ○ Work
- ○ Playing sports
- ○ Watching television

- ○ Renting movies
- ○ Working in my garden
- ○ Reading
- ○ Time with my pets

The secret of a happy marriage is simple:
Just keep on being as polite to one another as
you are to your best friends.

—ROBERT QUILLEN

When it comes to my career, I:
- ○ Am a workaholic
- ○ View work as a means to an end
- ○ Am a top-notch employee, but work is not my life
- ○ Do what I must to keep my job, but not much more

When it comes to family planning, I:
- ○ Believe in birth control
- ○ Believe in only natural birth control
- ○ Don't believe in birth control

If we experienced an unplanned pregnancy, I would:
- ○ Be scared and not tell my mate immediately
- ○ Put the baby up for adoption
- ○ Raise the baby and be thrilled
- ○ Ask my family to raise our child

If we had to put our child up for adoption, I would want the adoption to be:
- ○ An open adoption
- ○ A closed adoption

The main reason I want to have children is:
- ○ To carry on my family's name
- ○ To prove to the world that I am an adult
- ○ Because my friends have children
- ○ They are so wonderful—I love kids

In terms of child rearing, my parents were:
- ○ Strict disciplinarians
- ○ Very liberal
- ○ Middle-of-the-road

Tip: The more issues you solve before you marry, the less you will have to work out after the wedding.

I would love to have:
- ○ Only one child
- ○ Two children
- ○ Three children
- ○ Four or more children

There is no more lovely, friendly, and charming relationship, communion, or company than a good marriage.

—MARTIN LUTHER

I believe that children are:
- ○ The best thing that can happen to a couple
- ○ The main reason to get married
- ○ Marriage/romance spoilers
- ○ Not for me and my mate

I want to have only sons because:
- ○ Boys are easier to raise than girls
- ○ Boys are sports lovers like me
- ○ Boys are rougher and tougher

A man's house is his castle.

—SIR EDWARD COKE

I would prefer to have only daughters because:
- ○ Girls are closer to their families
- ○ Girls are less rambunctious
- ○ Girls are more emotional
- ○ Girls always look after their parents

Nobody tells you—many couples experience some form of adjustment period with their in-laws.

If my mate and I cannot have children of our own, we will:
- ○ Adopt
- ○ Probably separate

- ○ Be devastated
- ○ Become foster parents
- ○ Be an even better aunt and uncle

When I imagine myself as a parent I think that I will be:
- ○ A big pushover
- ○ A strict disciplinarian
- ○ Exactly like my parents
- ○ A blundering nutcase—I don't have a clue what to do as a parent

Tip: Always give your partner the benefit of the doubt.

I want to have children:
- ○ Within the next year
- ○ In two or three years
- ○ Someday
- ○ Only in my dreams

Before my mate and I have children, I:
- ○ Want to be happily married for a period of time
- ○ Want to talk to a family counselor
- ○ Want to be tested for genetic defects
- ○ Want to reach my career goals
- ○ Want to travel the world
- ○ Want to sow our wild oats

If my mate and I adopt a child, we would consider:
- ○ Foreign adoption
- ○ Domestic adoption

- ○ Biracial adoption
- ○ Adopting an older child
- ○ Adopting a foster child

If we hired a baby-sitter to take care of our children, I:
- ○ Would want references
- ○ Would hire a teenager from our neighborhood for the job
- ○ Would want the baby-sitter to be someone I know well

Tip: Always be articulate when you express your needs and wants to your mate.

The method of birth control that I prefer is:
- ○ Condoms
- ○ The pill
- ○ A diaphragm
- ○ The rhythm method
- ○ I don't believe in birth control

Tip: Always have a date night to keep the romantic part of your relationship alive and growing.

When it comes to meals, I want to:
- ○ Eat at home most nights
- ○ Grab junkfood on my way home from work

- ○ Sit down to a home-cooked meal
- ○ Dine out at lots of different restaurants
- ○ Find a mate that is a great chef

My dream honeymoon is a trip to:
- ○ Travel around the world
- ○ Paris in the springtime
- ○ The country of our ancestors
- ○ Hawaii or any tropical paradise
- ○ An exciting domestic city
- ○ A foreign destination
- ○ Anywhere with my mate

I believe that the most important part of being a wife is:
- ○ Being a partner to my mate
- ○ Making a lovely home
- ○ Becoming a mother
- ○ Earning a good salary
- ○ Being a great lover

Tip: The happiest of couples are those
who constantly work on
their relationships.

I feel that the most important part of being a husband is:
- ○ Being my wife's best friend
- ○ Becoming a father
- ○ Earning a good income
- ○ Being a great lover

During the week, I usually go to bed at:
- ○ 9:00 P.M.
- ○ 10:00 P.M.
- ○ Around 11:00 P.M.
- ○ Midnight
- ○ The wee small hours of the morning

*You mustn't force sex to do the work of love
or love to do the work of sex.*

—MARY MCCARTHY

When it comes to spending time by myself each week, I usually spend:
- ○ Several hours doing my own thing
- ○ Ten or more hours alone
- ○ Hardly any time by myself as I want to be around people

During the week, I get up at:
- ○ 6:00 A.M.
- ○ 7:00 A.M.
- ○ 8:00 A.M.
- ○ Mid-morning
- ○ Noon

*Tip: The happiest couples
regularly attend church together.*

For breakfast, I usually prepare:
- ○ Toast and coffee
- ○ A big breakfast
- ○ Cold cereal
- ○ Leftovers from the night before
- ○ Nothing—who has the time?

In the mornings, I spend this amount of time in the bathroom getting ready to go to work:
- ○ Fifteen minutes or less
- ○ About thirty minutes
- ○ Close to an hour
- ○ Longer than an hour

Tip: Be sure that you and your mate have a similar definition of commitment, if you want to be happy together for the rest of your lives.

When it comes to drinking, I:
- ○ Am a social drinker
- ○ Do not drink alcoholic beverages
- ○ Drink a lot and often
- ○ Am a recovering alcoholic

When it comes to drugs, I:
- ○ Have tried them, but don't regularly use them
- ○ Would never take any drugs
- ○ Use drugs somewhat regularly
- ○ Am a recovering addict

When it comes to smoking, I:
- ○ Do not smoke and I never will
- ○ Smoke regularly
- ○ Hate smoking
- ○ Smoke cigars
- ○ Smoke only during highly stressful times

Home life ceases to be free and beautiful as soon as it is founded on borrowing and debt.

—IBSEN

When it comes to being on time, I:
- ○ Am like a European train—prompt to a fault!
- ○ Run fairly closely to my schedule
- ○ Don't live by the clock
- ○ Am always running late

The best part of physical intimacy is kissing:
- ○ True
- ○ False

The best part of physical intimacy is snuggling:
- ○ True
- ○ False

The thing that I do that contaminates our relationship is:
- ○ I try to make my mate jealous
- ○ I am not always truthful
- ○ I fear commitment
- ○ I start arguments

- o I bait my mate during disagreements
- o I flirt with others

I like to sleep in:
- o Flannel pj's
- o The buff
- o Lovely lingerie
- o Sweats
- o Undies

Love is like a mushroom. You never know whether it's the real thing until it's too late.

—ANONYMOUS

When I think of lingerie, I envision:
- o Items out of a Victoria's Secret catalogue
- o Flannel granny gowns
- o Comfy pj's
- o Oversized T-shirts

Tip: The best lovers are creative and emotional.

I can best be described as:
- o An optimist
- o A pessimist
- o An average Joe

*It doesn't much signify whom one marries,
for one is sure to find out the next morning
that it was someone else.*

—*Samuel Rogers*

When I first wake up in the morning, I'm:
- ○ Up and ready to rock and roll
- ○ Cranky like a bear
- ○ Dead to world
- ○ In a trance
- ○ Content to stretch and plan my whole day while I'm still in bed

*Nobody tells you—most couples really do
"settle down" after marrying.*

With my present job, I usually work:
- ○ Less than forty hours per week
- ○ About forty hours
- ○ Around fifty hours
- ○ About sixty hours
- ○ More than sixty hours

I eat dinner:
- ○ On my way home from the office
- ○ As soon as I get home from work

○ When my spouse fixes it
○ Fashionably late in the evening
○ Whenever I am hungry

When it comes to financial arrangements between a couple, I believe:

○ Each partner should share all the financial responsibilities
○ Each partner should have total financial freedom—no reporting to one another about personal spending
○ The couple should work as a team and all financial decisions should be made together
○ That financial arrangements are for businesses only—we will just take things as they come along

When I want to unwind after a hard day at work, I:

○ Collapse on the couch
○ Soak in a hot tub
○ Nap
○ Go shopping
○ Play sports
○ Head to the gym
○ Call coworkers and talk about work
○ Snuggle with my mate
○ Call my friends
○ Play with my dog
○ Want to have sex

Tip: The quality of your relationship depends upon the degree to which both partners needs are being met.

Each week, I spend this amount of time going shopping:
- O Less than one hour
- O About two hours
- O Two to five hours
- O Hours and hours—I'm a shopaholic

I like to entertain friends at my home:
- O Weekly
- O Several times a month
- O About once a month
- O Only on big occasions
- O Whenever I feel in the mood
- O I don't like to entertain at home

Tip: Learn to enjoy, accept, and appreciate your differences.

I think that dining out at restaurants is:
- O For special occasions only
- O A modern convenience that I love
- O A treat after a hard day at the office
- O A big waste of money
- O Fun, quick, and easy

When it comes to former loves, I:
- O Like to keep in touch
- O Keep a low profile
- O Have nothing to hide from my current love
- O Am friends with all of them

○ Wish that they would quietly fall off the face of the Earth

---

Tip: Don't get married till you and your significant other are both ready emotionally, spiritually, and financially.

I like my mate to say romantic things to me:
- ○ Only during intimate moments
- ○ From time to time, but I'm not the mushy type
- ○ At least once a day
- ○ Nonstop—I'm a romantic!
- ○ Yuk—romance is for novels, not real life

---

*If your life at night is good,
you think you have everything.*

—EURIPIDES

When it comes to vacations, I:
- ○ Only want to travel with my mate
- ○ Want to take separate vacations from time to time
- ○ Always like to travel by myself

Bad reasons to get married:
You dislike being single.
You desperately want to be a parent.
You love weddings.
You fear that no one else will ever propose to you again.
You think that if things don't work out,
you can get a divorce.
Your best friend or sibling just got married.
You want two incomes instead of just yours alone.
You want to please your parents who
tell you to settle down.
Your ex-love just got married.

I plan to tell my mate:
- O Everything—we shouldn't have any secrets
- O Most everything—a little privacy is a good thing
- O Not too much—I'm a very private person

On a regular basis, I would like to receive, from my mate:
- O Flowers
- O Candy
- O Cards
- O Love letters
- O Notes
- O Gifts
- O Back rubs
- O Surprise getaways

- Telephone calls of a romantic nature
- Loving little touches

Men are never so likely to settle a question rightly as when they discuss it freely.

—*MACAULAY*

POINTS TO PONDER:

- Do my significant other and I have many things in common?
- Do we have good chemistry between us?
- What are the first three words that come into my mind when I think of my significant other?

Follow your bliss.

—*JOSEPH CAMPBELL*

- What are the first three words that come to my mind when I think of our relationship?
- How does my significant other treat himself?
- Am I caught up in planning the wedding and overlooking the quality of our relationship?
- Why do I want to get married?
- Do I really love this person? Could I just be settling instead of waiting for the right person to come along?

- Does my significant other truly love me? How do I know?

Perhaps the chief business of life is simply to learn how to love.

—MARSHA SINETAR

- Does my significant other enhance the quality of my life?

Choices are the hinges of destiny.

—EDWIN MARKHAM

- Does this relationship add more joy or more pain to my world?
- Does my significant other make me feel better or worse about myself?

What I cannot love, I overlook.

—ANAÏS NIN

- Are our life plans harmonious?
- My biggest fear about marriage is_____.
- My biggest concern about my significant
  other is _____.

People see only what they are prepared to see.
                                        —*RALPH BASY*

- Does my significant other treat me like an equal?
- Am I learning anything from my mate? What?
- Will we have a prenuptial agreement?
- Has our relationship ever been abusive in any way?
- Are we both willing to work at our relationship?

As soon as you trust yourself,
you will know how to live.

                                        —*GOETHE*

- Is my mate a flirt? Am I a flirt?

The faultfinder will find faults even in paradise.
                                —*HENRY DAVID THOREAU*

- Does my significant other want a partner or a parent?
- What issues does my mate bring to the relationship? What ones do I bring?
- Is my significant other too possessive?
- How do we resolve arguments?
- Does my mate hold a grudge? Do I?

If you deny yourself commitment,
what can you do with your life?

—HARVEY FIERSTEIN

- Have I met all of my significant other's friends and family?

The bravest are the tenderest—
The loving are the daring.

—BAYARD TAYLOR

- What do I think of my mate's friends?
- Can my mate take care of himself/herself?
- Does my significant other respect me?
- Am I proud of my significant other?

*It always fills us with happiness when we know
we are truly loved by one we dearly love.*

—JOHNNY GRUELLE

- Does my mate support my dreams and goals?
- Is my significant other faithful to me and to our relationship?

Doubt whom you will, but never yourself.

—CHRISTIAN BOREE

- Do we share the same expectations about marriage?
- Can I accept my mate's choice of friends?

Decisions determine destiny.

—FREDERICK SPEAKMAN

- How do my mate's parents treat each other?

Life is a romantic business,
but you have to make the romance.
—OLIVER WENDELL HOLMES

- In my heart of hearts, does this relationship feel right to me?
- Am I rushing our relationship?
- Do I really like my significant other, as well as love her/him?

To get the full value of a joy you must
have somebody to divide it with.

—MARK TWAIN

- Can I picture myself being faithful to this person for the rest of my life?
- Can I keep my part of the marriage vows?
- Do I truly believe that my significant other will be there for me in good times, as well as the bad times?
- How does my significant other handle conflict, trials, and hardships?
- Would I really want to have children with this person?
- Do we know how to fight the fair fight?

One is very crazy when in love.
—SIGMUND FREUD

- Do I expect our love to flourish or diminish after marriage?
- What areas in our relationship give me cause for concern?
- Have we ever broken up? Why? Why do I think things will be different in the future?

Marriage resembles a pair of shears, so joined that they cannot be separated, often moving in opposite directions, yet always punishing anyone who comes between them.
—SYDNEY SMITH

- Are we in agreement in matters of sex?

In a united marriage, happiness springs of itself.
—CHINESE PROVERB

- How long have we been together? What would happen if we had to wait a year or two to get married?
- How do I think my mate will change in the future? Can I live happily with those changes?

Our belief at the beginning of a doubtful undertaking is the one thing that ensures the successful outcome of our venture.

—WILLIAM JAMES

- Have we fully discussed all of the responsibilities that come along with marriage?
- Do we concur in financial matters?
- What is the best thing about our relationship?
- What is the worst part of our relationship?
- Have we considered the very real fact that people always change after marriage?
- Do we have a spiritual foundation for our relationship?

Grow old with me! The best is yet to be.

—ROBERT BROWNING

- If my significant other has an ex-spouse, can I deal with this person in a healthy manner?

The difference between love and lust is like the difference between strolling and skiing.
—*LEO ROSTEN*

- How do our parents' marriages affect our ideas about romantic relationships?
- Is my significant other good to me?
- Are we always honest with each other?
- Is my significant other over her/his old loves? Am I over all of mine?
- Has my significant other been married before? If so, why did it end?

Love is the triumph of imagination over intelligence.
—*H. L. MENCKEN*

- Could I stand by my mate in tragedy? Would my mate stand by me?

Uncertainty and mystery are energies of life.
Don't let them scare you unduly,
for they keep boredom at bay and
spark creativity.

—*R. I. FITZHENRY*

- If my mate has children, can I build a healthy relationship with them?
- What would I change about my mate if I could change anything about him/her?
- Do we often laugh together?
- Would I be willing to move to be with my significant other?
- What do I love most about our relationship?

A hunch is creativity trying to tell you something.

—*ANONYMOUS*

- Am I proud to be seen with my significant other?

*American women expect to find in their husbands
a perfection that English women only hope to
find in their butlers.*

—W. SOMERSET MAUGHAM

- Does my significant other trust me?
- Does my significant other always keep his/her promises?
- Does my mate have a healthy sense of self-esteem?
- Do I think that we will grow in different directions?
- Does my significant other have a flaw that I simply cannot tolerate?

Love: the only fire for which there is no insurance.

—ANONYMOUS

- How often do we argue?
- Is there one issue that we fight about over and over again?

Nothing ventured, nothing gained.

—ANONYMOUS

- Is my partner too needy? Am I?

You don't just luck into things...
You build step by step, whether it's
friendships or opportunities.

—*BARBARA BUSH*

- Does my significant other give me the right amount of physical affection?
- Do I fantasize about other loves?
- Do I feel that there is something missing in our relationship?
- If my significant other has children, am I comfortable and satisfied with my place in my mate's list of priorities?
- Have we gone for premarital counseling?
- Would I be happy if our children turned out to be like my significant other?

The conclusions of passion are the only reliable ones.

—*KIERKEGAARD*

- Do I view my partner as a diamond in the rough that I plan to change over time?

Getting divorced just because you don't love a man is almost as silly as getting married just because you do.

—ZSA ZSA GABOR

- Have we discussed in depth *all* of the major components of married life?
- Do I have any doubts about this relationship? What are they?
- Have we talked about all of the issues involved with having a family?
- Are we from similar backgrounds? If not, will our differences be difficult for us to manage?
- Do we enjoy sharing all aspects of our lives, or do we feel crowded in certain areas?

He that seeks trouble always finds it.

—ENGLISH PROVERB

- What does parenting mean to my significant other?

An archaeologist is the best husband a woman can have; the older she gets, the more interested he is in her.

—AGATHA CHRISTIE

- Do I expect our sex life to diminish over time?
- Do I feel comfortable with his/her family? Can I accept them as my new family?

Marriage is a very good thing, but I think it's a mistake to make a habit of it.

—W. SOMERSET MAUGHAM

- Am I mature enough to handle a long-term relationship?
- Do I enjoy just being together with my partner, or do I feel that I need to be entertained?
- How soon do we want to get married? Why then?
- Does my significant other have his/her temper under control?
- Does my significant other easily express his/her feelings for me or is he/she stingy with his/her affection?
- Have I fallen in love too fast? If so, what is the hurry?

*The magic of first love is our
ignorance that it can ever end.*

—*BENJAMIN DISRAELI*

- What do my friends and family members think about our relationship?

*There are few people who are not ashamed of their
love affairs when the infatuation is over.*

—*LA ROCHEFOUCAULD*

- Have I ever caught my partner in a lie?
- Have I ever suspected that my significant other cheated on me?
- Do we share harmonious religious beliefs? If not, can we accept our differences?
- How do my furry friends feel about my significant other?
- Why do I want to get married?

Always be a little kinder than necessary.

—*SIR JAMES M. BARRIE*

- Do I believe in romantic love lasting for a lifetime?
- Am I being pressured into getting married by my significant other, friends, or family members?
- Do I feel connected to my significant other even when we are apart?

He is happiest, be he king or peasant,
who finds peace in his home.

—GOETHE

- Do I know all about my significant other's past?

How casually and unobservedly we make
all our most valued acquaintances.

—RALPH WALDO EMERSON

- Does my significant other possess the qualities that are most important to me?
- What sacrifices am I willing to make for my mate?

Friendships, like marriages,
are dependent on avoiding the unforgivable.

—JOHN D. MACDONALD

- Do my significant other and I clearly understand about each other's financial picture?
- Will my partner change if I asked her/him to?
- Am I in love with my partner for the way he/she is or for his potential?
- Is my significant other controlled by his/her parents in any manner?
- Does my significant other need to be rescued emotionally or financially?
- Do I trust my significant other with my heart, finances, friends, worldly goods, pets, children, and life?
- After working through the questions in this book, do I still want to build a future with my significant other?

What greater thing is there for two human souls than to find that they are joined for life.

—*GEORGE ELIOT*

2002 Romantic Ideas
$5.95, 144 pages
ISBN: 1-55850-819-8

2002 Things to Do on a Date
$5.95, 144 pages
ISBN: 1-58062-079-5

2002 Ways to Say
"I Love You"
$5.95, 144 pages
ISBN: 1-58062-080-9

2002 Ways to Find, Attract,
and Keep a Mate
$5.95, 144 pages
ISBN: 1-58062-081-7

Available wherever books are sold.

For more information, or to order, call 800-872-5627 or visit www.adamsmedia.com

Adams Media Corporation, 260 Center Street, Holbrook, MA 02343